What Else Can I Pl
Violin
Grade Three

© International Music Publications Ltd
First published in 1996 by International Music Publications Ltd
International Music Publications Ltd is a Faber Music company
Bloomsbury House 74–77 Great Russell Street London WC1B 3DA
Series Editor: Mark Mumford
Cover designed by Lydia Merrills-Ashcroft
Music arranged and processed by Barnes Music Engraving Ltd
Printed in England by Caligraving Ltd
All rights reserved

ISBN10: 0-571-53062-1
EAN13: 978-0-571-53062-5

To buy Faber Music publications or to find out about the full range of titles available,
please contact your local music retailer or Faber Music sales enquiries:

Faber Music Ltd, Burnt Mill, Elizabeth Way, Harlow, CM20 2HX England
Tel: +44(0)1279 82 89 82   Fax: +44(0)1279 82 89 83
sales@fabermusic.com   fabermusic.com

Introduction

In this *What Else Can I Play?* collection you'll find sixteen popular tunes that are both challenging and entertaining.

The pieces have been carefully selected and arranged to create ideal supplementary material for young violinists who are either working towards or have recently taken a Grade Three violin examination.

As the student progresses through the volume, technical demands increase and new concepts are introduced which reflect the requirements of the major Examination Boards. Suggestions and guidelines on bowing, fingering, dynamics and tempo are given for each piece, together with technical tips and performance notes.

Pupils will experience a wide variety of music, ranging from folk and classical through to showtunes and popular songs, leading to a greater awareness of musical styles.

Whether it's for light relief from examination preparation, or to reinforce the understanding of new concepts, this collection will enthuse and encourage all young violin players.

Turkey in the straw

Traditional

My love she's but a lassie yet

Traditional

Johnny Todd

Traditional

Blow the man down

Traditional

My favorite things

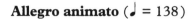

Words by Oscar Hammerstein II, Music by Richard Rodgers

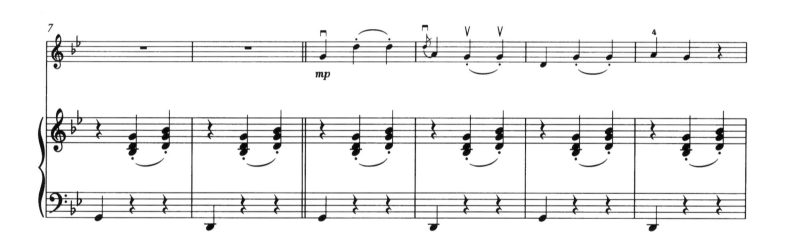

Mistletoe and wine

Words by Leslie Stewart and Jeremy Paul, Music by Keith Strachan

Peermusic (UK) Ltd, London WC1X 8LZ

Over the rainbow

Words by E Y Harburg, Music by Harold Arlen

Drusilla Penny

Richard Carpenter and John Bettis

Waltzing in the clouds

Words by Gus Kahn, Music by Robert Stolz

18

The entertainer

Scott Joplin

to Coda ⊕

22

Hungarian dance No. 5

Johannes Brahms

Blueberry Hill

Words and Music by Al Lewis, Larry Stock and Vincent Rose

Java jive

Words by Milton Drake, Music by Ben Oakland

The Christmas song
(Chestnuts roasting on an open fire)

Words and Music by Mel Torme and Robert Wells

A foggy day

Music and Lyrics by George Gershwin and Ira Gershwin

A nightingale sang in Berkeley Square

Words by Eric Maschwitz, Music by Manning Sherwin